Beyond Casseroles is inspiratior
meaningful. Lisa's "505 ways" w
but for a chronically ill friend, it
needed. It v ... ' ... laugh

It will make

DATE DUE

everyone a
away with
(though, yc
may chang
Zanina Jac
Disability /

From the
the seriou
joyfully, d
tips for b
for all chu
Vonda SI
Unmaski

When w
has not :
anything
problem
quick fli
ideas, ai

Demco

I can do that. ......,
Gloria Cassity Stargel, Author, *The Healing, One
Family's Victorious Struggle With Cancer*,
Contributing Author, *Chicken Soup for the
Father/Son Soul*

Someone with a broken bone or young baby needs help—but short-term. Those with chronic conditions may need assistance and support for much longer. *Beyond Casseroles* provides creative suggestions for how to be truly useful to someone whose need doesn't go away.
Sarah Whitman, Pain Management Psychiatrist and author of the website and blog, *How to Cope with Pain.org*

I love *Beyond Casseroles!* I recommend it to every person who has a friend with a disability and wants to know how they can help them. I would love to give them out to the women in our church.
Pat Capasso lives with chronic illness and volunteers with Joni and Friends Greater Philadelphia

Lisa Copen has again translated the pain, isolation, and emotions of chronic illness into a format that can be understood and utilized by anyone. Through her mix of heartfelt wisdom, personal experience, and humor, she's written a book offering real and pragmatic advice for helping friends and family. I recommend this for anyone who wants to understand how to reach out to a friend or family member with chronic illness. Before baking them another casserole, read this book!
Dr. William July & Jamey Lacy July
Co-authors of *A Husband, A Wife, & An Illness: Living Life Beyond Chronic Illness*

The thought of encouraging someone who is hurting seems easy. So why don't we do it? Lisa Copen's practical, well thought-out book gives us easy ways to do what God has called each of us to do. Once you start reading you'll think 'That's great, why didn't I think of it?' Get ready to step into the gap and minister!
Ken Chambers, Director of Church Relations, Joni and Friends

To be fully present in another's life. To listen and to show compassion. To share with love and openness. These are gifts of grace. *Beyond Casseroles* tells us how these gifts can be given. It is a gift that will enlighten us all.
Rev. Michael Gingerich, Cancer Recovery Foundation of America, Co-author of *The Cancer Conqueror with Bible Study*

Beyond Casseroles is a loving instruction manual for both the giver and the receiver—the lessons of caring and love abound—and the messages of hope, acceptance, love and healing are a balm for the soul. Having spare copies to share of this must-have book is one of my strategies for helping those trying to cope with chronic illness. Rest assured,
I'm keeping one for me and my family to share!
Nancy Derby, RN, BSN, MSEd, VP Executive Board of Directors, National Fibromyalgia Association

Everyone knows someone who grieves or is chronically ill. Many struggle with knowing how to help or what to say. This is the only book you need. It will teach you to be an expert encourager. Fantastic!
Angela Posey-Arnold, author of *The Nightingale Protocol: A Handbook of Hope for Nurses And Caregivers*, RN, BSN

Beyond Casseroles is full of ideas and things to say or not say that will unequivocally help you be the kind of person you want to be to your hurting friends.
Copen has given wonderful ways to encourage those who suffer to feel more valuable and useful as well as loved and cared for. This book is a treasure.
Jo Franz, National Speaker and author of *Soar Unafraid: Learning to Trust No Matter What*

Lisa Copen, the author of *Beyond Casseroles: 505 Ways to Encourage a Chronically Ill Friend* gives many creative ideas for ministering to the chronically ill in such a way that gives joy, hope, and a stronger sense of self worth people may have lost due to the challenges of their illness and pain.
Missy Brenton, HopeKeepers® leader of Ocilla United Methodist Church, Ocilla, Georgia

With all these great tips and ideas, *Beyond Casseroles* is long overdue.
Rebekah Montgomery, editor of *Right to the Heart of Women*

Fear of the unknown keeps most people from helping those who suffer. *Beyond Casseroles'* moves us out of the fear zone into the free zone. Lisa Copen's work benefits all who want to minister to the suffering.
Rev. Dan'l C. Markham, Managing Director, Joni and Friends

As someone who lives with chronic illness, I often wonder how to respond when someone says, "Let me know if you need anything." Thanks to Lisa Copen, I've found the perfect response in her powerful little book, *Beyond Casseroles*.
Judy Gann, Author of *The God of All Comfort: Devotions of Hope for Those Who Chronically Suffer*

I am currently caring for my mother under hospice care. People who come to visit never seem to know what to say. What an excellent book to have in one's living room to help them with things to say and not to say. I am also one with chronic pain. I have heard a lot of things from people that have really hurt when I am sure they were not meant to. Hopefully, this book will help alleviate those comments.
Diane L. Keil, Newport, MN

Those with chronic illness can themselves be motivated to assist others using this little activity-packed book. A must-read for everyone who desires to "serve one another in love."
Jonnie Wright, author, *The Silver Bullet: God's Rx for Chronic Pain*

This book helps remove a lot of the guesswork and awkwardness. As a single mom who struggles with burnout, this book jumpstarted my confidence by giving me tangible, doable ways to reach out and connect with some friends whose ongoing struggles limit their energy and mobility. I appreciate that the ideas are not about trying to "fix" my problems, but rather about finding ways to connect with me in the context of the realities I live with.
Dana Whiteacre

What a great compilation of wonderful ideas to show love and support to someone who is suffering with a chronic illness. I live with illness and specifically loved the part where Copen suggests people should offer to help even if others live in the home. My 84-year-old mother lives with my husband and I; He helps as much as he can but it would be super to have a woman help with some things I can no longer do—tasks that really need a woman's touch.
Linda Clarke

As the parent of a child with a chronic illness, I've heard just about every comment on my child's condition and my handling of it. Even though I am a caregiver, as the director of a ministry to families affected by special needs, I find myself referring to the book when my staff and I run out of blessings of share! Thank you!
Lisa Mattheiss, Executive Director LifeLine, Inc., Chattanooga, TN

Having fibromyalgia, I enjoyed reading *Beyond Casseroles* and finding helpful hints on how to help those in need. This book helps to take focus off of self and to think about others in need.
Vickie Niedrauer

This is a wonderful new book for people with chronic illness to use, as well as non-ill people. I plan on starting a chronic illness bible study at my church. This is another great tool that Lisa has put to our disposal.
Carla Rowley

This is such an inspirational treasure for friends, family, those in the medical field, and churches, as well as the person who is chronically ill. Thanks Lisa, you have given us a very special gift and tool in helping those we care about.
Jill Brownback

Wow! What a terrific book! Every church office should have a copy. As a church secretary it is hard to know how to help someone who is chronically ill. Of course, the question is always, "Is there anything we can help you with?" This book gives you ideas to encourage without asking. It is like a book of *surprises!*
Lisa S. Shutt Secretary, Berean Baptist Church

Wow! Lisa put words to the feelings I have. I love her lists, and the quotes are an inspiration to not only the chronically ill, but to everyone, who can pull away with words of wisdom.
Lori Kirl

You'll find more meaningful ways to show you care than you can imagine—cheer up your friend, provide practical help, show empathy, help her spiritually. It is so refreshing to read the suggestions of what not to do. It is so easy to say or do the wrong thing, to pity him, or to treat your friend like he can't think for herself. Copen's book provides not only pointers of how to assist in ways we may never have considered, but thought-provoking counsel for people who desire to help those who need comfort and support.
Connie Roberts Coordinator, Chronic Illness Support Group of Dayspring Church & Blogger

As a life coach and chronic illness sufferer myself, I can honestly say that Copen's book offers a wealth of practical ideas for encouraging and ministering to those with a chronic illness. It's heart-warming, down-to-earth style and creative content make it an invaluable resource! ...truly inspirational!
Angela Dobbins, Life Coach/Director True Life Family Ministries

As a nurse, I often deal with family members who are at a loss to demonstrate love to a chronically ill loved one. As a patient, I wish I could be the recipient of such thoughtful and practical ways to live out love. Either way, you will be blessed! This is a must-have book for anyone who has wanted to do more for a chronically ill loved one, but needs inspiring ideas. Fabulous!
Debbie Lillo, Director of Family Support, Green Pastures, Inc.

As one reads Lisa's book, one quickly comes to the realization of what a chronically ill person endures daily. Family members, close friends, work colleagues—everyone can benefit from reading this book from a learning angle. Lisa Copen beautifully provides 505 ways to be a blessing to an ill friend and in the process assists the reader in a self-help lesson of patience, humility and appreciation of others' situations.

Julie Anne Silva, Owner of Lupie Bin

Beyond Casseroles will help you to understand the challenges that individuals with chronic illnesses face and how to minister to their needs. This book is full of simple, practical, and creative ways to help. As someone who suffers from a chronic illness, I can say that the ideas presented in this book are excellent.

Rachel Lundy, disabled wife and mother

Beyond Casseroles outlines thoughtful, practical ideas to touch the heart and warm the soul of those who are chronically ill. It's a must-read for those who want to demonstrate they care but want suggestions on how.

Angela Vittucci, R.D./DHS Registered Dietitian; Digestive Health Specialist

beyond
casseroles

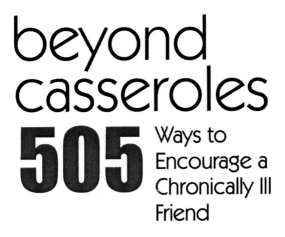

505 Ways to Encourage a Chronically Ill Friend

Conquering the Confusions
of Chronic Illness Series

Lisa J. Copen

Rest Ministries Publishers
SAN DIEGO, CA

Request for information should be sent to:
Rest Ministries, Publishers
Rest Ministries, Inc., Joyfully serving the chronically ill
Ask about our HopeKeepers® Magazine and
National Invisible Chronic Illness Awareness Week
PO Box 502928, San Diego, CA 29150
858-486-4685; Toll-free 888-751-REST (7378)
Web site: www.restministries.org
Email: rest@restministries.org

"When we honestly ask ourselves which person in our lives means the most to us, we often find that it is those who, instead of giving advice, solutions, or cures, have chosen rather to share our pain and touch our wounds with a warm and tender hand. The friend who can be silent with us in a moment of despair or confusion, who can stay with us in an hour of grief and bereavement, who can tolerate not knowing, not curing, not healing and face with us the reality of our powerlessness, that is a friend who cares." ~Henri Nouwen

Many of us have a helpful heart. If you are reading this book it is likely that you have a sincere desire to reach out to people who are hurting. Perhaps you are concerned about a friend's situation and wish to learn how to encourage her better. You may be someone who encourages people daily through your field of work. Maybe you have an illness yourself and you understand how vital encouragement is to one's emotional well-being. Regardless, we are each commanded to "encourage one another daily" (Hebrews 3:13). So where do we begin?

Most of us want to express our concern when we see someone hurting; however, words seem so hollow. Rather than offering trite bits of encouragement that don't express our compassion, we have been known to procrastinate. Maybe we drop by her house with a casserole, but before we know it, weeks have passed and then months. We really do care but now we feel embarrassed that we didn't visit sooner or that we didn't call.

We rationalize, "*Surely she has other friends who have offered her support during this trying time. I'm sure I wasn't even missed. I don't have the time to do much for her anyway.*" But in our hearts we know that we've missed an opportunity to simply let someone know that she matters to us.

....

You no longer have to wonder how to show someone with a chronic illness that you care. Just flip to any page in this little book and start reading. You'll soon be inspired by simple yet meaningful ways to reach out to someone. Don't be overwhelmed—you aren't expected to fulfill all 505 ideas, but I hope that you will be optimistic about how easy it is to express your compassion.

Often we just say, "Let me know if you need anything," but if you have ever needed help you know just how difficult it can be to ask someone to run an errand for you, much less change your sheets! Get creative and give a "gift certificate" with a task that one can "redeem" anytime. It's a fun way to make sure one knows you really mean it when you say, "I'm glad to help," and it also makes your friend feel much more comfortable asking for assistance. See the back page for a certificate you can copy and fill in, or just make up your own.

The *Merriam-Webster Dictionary* defines "encourage" as "to inspire with courage, spirit, or hope; to spur on; to give help or patronage to." We all have the responsibility to inspire another, and we'll discover in the end that we're blessed beyond measure.

1. Ask, "What events in your life are changing and how are you coping with the changes?"

2. Understand that she lives in a constant state of making decisions for which there is no guarantee that she is making the right choice.

3. Put meals in disposable containers and attach a note saying "This doesn't need to be returned."

4. Add stickers to envelopes for a cheerful touch.

5. Arrange for your friend's kids to have a night with your children.

6. Don't make a person into a project.

7. Ask, "Would you be willing to talk to a friend of mine who has recently been diagnosed with a chronic illness and offer her some encouragement?" It makes one feel good to know that her experience can offer someone else hope and that God still has a purpose for her life.

8. Wash his car and put a little note inside for him to find later.

9. Remember important anniversaries, both the good and the bad. No one else will.

10. Ask, "Do you want company the day that you wait for the test results? I could come over for a couple of hours."

"No matter how little you have, you can always give some of it away." ~Catherine Marshall

11. Just listen . . . until it hurts to not say anything. And then listen some more.

12. Ask her, "How do you feel God is working through—or despite—this illness in your life? I'm interested."

13. Ask, "What do you wish people understood about your illness?"

14. Don't make her feel guilty about things that she cannot do.

15. Treat her to a gift of movie rentals via postal mail through a service ($7-15 a month).

16. Ask, "Would you be comfortable with having your name on a prayer list, so that others can pray for you?" Don't assume.

17. Instead of saying, "I will pray for you," say, "I'd like to pray for you right now, if that's okay."

18. Mop the floors.

19. Ask if she would be interested in writing something for the church newsletter, maybe even about the subject of living with chronic illness.

20. Buy a brightly colored umbrella as a gift.

"A good friend is a connection to life -
a tie to the past, a road to the future, the key to sanity
in a totally insane world." ~Lois Wyse

....

21. Ask, "Do you have an errand I can run for you before coming over?"

22. Ask her to do spontaneous things, like go to a concert in the park, or just for a picnic. She may be more likely to participate since she knows if it's a good day or a bad day.

23. Don't say, "So, why aren't you healed yet?" or "I wonder what God is trying to teach you that you just aren't learning!"

24. For a unique gift, provide brightly colored paper plates, napkins, and utensils in a gift bag with a note that says "For when you don't feel like doing dishes."

25. Get her a pretty box to keep all of her notes of encouragement. Remind her to get it out and read things when she is feeling down.

26. Be her advocate. If you are at an event and walking/seating is an issue because of her disability, ask her if she'd like you to take care of it. If she says you can, be firm but not rude. Don't embarrass her by making accusations of discrimination or by making a scene.

....

27. Ask, "Would you be interested in a prayer partner from our church?"

28. Purchase matching coffee mugs for you and your friend, and then commit to pray for one another each morning while using them.

29. Say, "While you're in the hospital I'd be happy to take care of your pet."

30. Don't tell her about your brother's niece's cousin's best friend who tried a cure for the same illness and. . . (you know the rest).

31. Find out which charity is most important to her and then give a donation in her honor.

32. Ask, "What are your top three indulgences?" and then spoil her soon.

33. Hold the door open for her. They are heavy!

34. Don't tease her and call her "hop along" or "slowpoke." Comments you mean in fun can cut to the quick and destroy her spirit. Proverbs 18:14 says, "A man's spirit sustains him in sickness, but a crushed spirit who can bear?"

35. Say, "I know you must need someone to just vent to occasionally. I may not fully understand how you feel, but I'm here to listen anytime."

36. Ask your church youth group to come over and clean up the yard during seasonal changes.

37. Don't ask her, "How are you able to make it financially?" If she wants to share a burden she will.

38. Ask, "What would you advise me to look for in a new doctor?"

39. If your friend has a disabled parking placard and you are driving, allow her to tell you where she wants to park. If she's feeling particularly good that day, she may not want to park in the "blue space." Don't be disappointed that you'll have to walk farther.

40. Don't gossip about others. She'll wonder what you say about her. "Do not let any unwholesome talk come out of your mouths, but only what is helpful for building others up according to their needs, that it may benefit those who listen" (Ephesians 4:29).

Proverbs 25:11 says,
"A word aptly spoken is like apples of gold in settings of silver." Be kind, gentle, and respectful.

41. Accept that her chronic illness may not go away. If she's accepting it, don't tell her the illness is winning and she's giving in to it.

42. Don't say, "Let me know if there is anything I can do." People rarely feel comfortable saying, "Yes, my laundry." Instead pick something you are willing to do and then ask her permission. Try the coupon in back!

43. Ask her to share her testimony at an event.

44. Buy a magazine subscription for her on her favorite topic.

45. Plant a rosebush to view from a window.

46. Understand that you don't need to know all of the details about the illness in order to be helpful. He'll share with you what he's comfortable with you knowing.

47. Don't ask, "Why can't the doctors help you?" or insinuate that it must be in her head. There are millions of people who are in pain with illnesses that do not have cures.

48. Avoid having gifts be "pity gifts." Just say, "I saw these flowers and their cheerfulness reminded me of you."

49. Send tapes of church services your friend misses to her with a copy of the bulletin and a note.

50. If she doesn't have a cordless phone, get her one. Phone headsets are also nice.

51. Don't tease her about how long she spends in the bathroom. She wouldn't be there if she didn't need to be.

52. Ask, "Are your symptoms predictable or not? How does that affect your life?"

53. Do not reassure her that God can heal all illnesses if one has enough faith. People with illness know God is capable of healing. Do remind her that God knows and cares.

54. If she receives financial disability assistance don't say, "Well, aren't you lucky! Boy, would I like to just sit and back and collect a check."

55. Before he comes home from the hospital, stock the refrigerator and freezer with meals that are labeled and have easy directions attached.

56. Respect her prayer requests. Don't dismiss her concerns and pray for her healing in front of her if she's just requested specific prayer for new medications.

57. Withhold from sharing every "cure" you've heard of for his illness. He's bombarded with cures and needs you to be his refuge from that.

58. If your friend misses a special event in your life, call and say, "I wondered if I could bring some photos over and share it with you. You're very special to me, and you were part of this day whether you were there or not."

"Each of us may be sure that if God sends us
on stony paths He will provide us with strong shoes, and
He will not send us out on any journey for which
He does not equip us well."
~Alexander Maclaren

59. Say, "I'd like to bring you dinner next week. Would Monday or Tuesday night be better?"

60. Never invite her to go Christmas shopping with you just so you can use her disabled parking placard.

61. Don't tell her, "If you didn't overdo it, then you wouldn't be in so much pain!"

62. Ask, "Are you up for a visit?" before you arrive.

63. Don't say, "Well, you've had a good life—more than a lot of people can hope for," as if it's all downhill from here.

64. If someone your friend loves passes away, offer to accompany and drive her to the memorial service. She's going to need your emotional and physical support, but grieving is important.

65. Ask your church to add more disabled parking places. There are never enough.

66. Never give a power squeeze when you shake his hand. Be gentle. You have nothing to prove.

67. Bring her family meals when she is in the hospital, not just after she gets out. Include items for breakfasts, lunches, and snacks for the kids too.

68. Never say, "I know just how you feel!" even if you are absolutely positive that you do.

69. Recognize that medications can make people completely irrational at times; give her the benefit of the doubt that it could be the drugs speaking and not your friend.

70. Don't tell her you "need to get some rest and I'm sure you will feel much better." Rest won't cure her illness.

71. Drop by her house with a fancy cup of hot tea or coffee on a dreary rainy day and tell her you were thinking of her.

72. Don't tell her how hard children are to raise and she shouldn't consider it with her illness.

73. When she says, "I'm fine," say, "No, I mean, how are you *really*? I know what fine means" and smile. . . .

74. Be aware of his favorite books and pick them up when you see them.

75. Don't say, "Well, it could be a lot worse" and then share a depressing story about someone else you know.

76. Romans 1:12 says, "That you and I may be mutually encouraged by each other's faith." Remember you will both encourage and be encouraged.

77. If you attend an event together and she needs to use a wheelchair, push it without insisting that "you could just get the electric one and drive yourself around."

78. Don't ever talk down to him as though he is a child.

79. Reflect on what friends have done for you when you've not felt well, and then do these things for others.

When feeling like you can't make a difference, reflect on this: "If you think you are too small to be effective, you have never been in bed with a mosquito."
~Betty Reese

80. Respect where he is with his faith. If you see him struggling, be sensitive; don't say, "Snap out of it! God is still good!" Pray for him silently and be patient with his walk.

81. Ask her if she wants to house-sit when you are on vacation. New surroundings may feel like a mini-vacation.

82. When she says she doesn't feel like she is being a good wife or mom, remind her that every woman feels this way at some point, and all God wants is for her to do the best she can and surrender the rest over to Him.

83. Ask her opinion on what books she would recommend to people who are suffering.

84. If she's hesitant to accept meals, just drop by with some "extra" and say, "I made a lot more than I should have and it's just too much for my family." (It's okay if you both know that's a stretch.)

85. Be an advocate for the chronically ill in your church. Ask for comfortable seating, care groups, special prayer time, and awareness about disability/illness issues.

86. Paint an "encouragement" bulletin board bright yellow for her and ask her where to hang it. She can add mail, photos— whatever will cheer her up when she is feeling down.

87. Bring her a poster of something bright for a bedroom wall.

88. Be aware that some people cope with illness by spending time alone and others by becoming very social. There is not a right way or a wrong way to cope—just different.

"The challenge of hospitality, both personally and professionally, comes when we are stressed out or tired and we offer it grudgingly. The gift of hospitality comes when we find in the welcoming face of hospitality the welcoming face of God."
~Cornelius Plantinga Jr.

89. Just hold her hand.

90. For a splurge, buy her sheets with a high thread count. They'll feel heavenly, and she'll appreciate you every time she climbs into bed.

91. Don't say, "What do you mean you're depressed? What's wrong now?"

....

92. Remember, nobody cares how much you know until they know how much you care.

93. If it seems like something dramatic is always going on in her life, it just may be. Drug shortages, injuries, insurance issues—each are life-changing, and people with illness feel out of control most of the time.

94. Respect her need for privacy and personal space. Don't assume that she is lucky to have you as a friend and should always drop everything to accommodate your need to extend kindness.

95. Never question if your friend is exaggerating her pain level. Regardless of what level it actually is, she is in pain and it's real to her so acknowledge it.

96. Teach your children not to kick people's wheelchairs.

97. "A friend loves at all times" (Proverbs 17:17a) . . . not just happy times.

98. Don't look up the side effects to all of the drugs she is taking and then give her the bad news.

....

She already knows, but the consequences of not taking the drugs may be even worse.

99. Recognize how God uses suffering to build character. See your friend as a source of wisdom God has placed into your path.

100. Don't say, "If you are *that* sick, you should be in a nursing home."

101. Never visit her if you think you may be getting a cold. If in doubt, just give her a call instead.

102. Ask her, "If someone volunteered to come by and pick up your house and make the coffee, would you be interested in hosting a Bible study or book club or some other group at your house occasionally?"

103. If you think, *someone should do that,* that may be God's way of calling you!

104. Be aware of the fact that illness is not just a matter of attitude. Don't say, "When are you going to get rid of that cane?" or "Did you know that illness is caused by stress?" Positive thinking doesn't always make the pain go away.

105. Take her driving around to see the Christmas lights.

106. When she says she's tired, she doesn't mean she is sleepy. She means she could lie down and sleep for a week solid and still wake up feeling like she has the flu.

"Human beings, all over the earth, have this curious idea that they ought to behave in a certain way, and can't really get rid of it." ~C. S. Lewis

107. Respect his choice to decide what he can and cannot do. If he wants to play golf today and be bedridden tomorrow, he's made that decision because it may be best for his mental state of mind.

108. A phone card is a nice gift to add to a card.

....

109. Don't say, "You look great!" If she does, it invalidates the pain. If she doesn't, she knows you're lying. Either way you can't win.

110. A dozen roses won't impress her, but a dandelion each month will help her feel special.

111. Write in a card, "I will continue to pray for you and ask Him in His wisdom to watch over you and keep you safe. You don't need to respond; I just wanted to let you know that you are not alone."

112. Pray for his family's finances and his job. He's worried about both and likely won't share these concerns with anyone.

113. When the grocery store has two turkeys for the price of one, call her to see if she could use the extra. Better yet, offer to cook it.

114. Get your hair done at the same time.

115. Tell her you are happy to be listed as an emergency number for her.

116. Take her kids for a movie and ice cream.

"Friendship improves happiness and abates misery, by the doubling of our joy and the dividing of our grief."
~Marcus Tullius Cicero

117. When she's in the hospital volunteer to stay with her a couple of hours so that her spouse/caregiver can go home and get a shower and have a bit of personal time knowing she's in your hands.

118. Remember, pain makes people more grouchy than they ever thought possible.

119. Buy her a gift subscription to *HopeKeepers Magazine* for people who live with chronic illness.

120. Don't say, "I told you so"—even if you did.

121. Ask, "What decisions do you have to make that I can pray about for you?"

122. According to research, larger churches put a lower priority on congregational care ministries than smaller churches. Try to change this!

123. Make plans with her in advance so she has something to look forward to, but understand if she still has to cancel.

124. Make sure she has an answering machine so she can screen calls when she doesn't feel well.

125. Search for a connection—a hobby, a style of music you both enjoy, or a past experience.

126. Don't wear perfume around her, especially if you know it can cause a reaction.

127. Never say, "You shouldn't feel that way!"

128. Understand that Christians *do* get depressed, and it's not sinful to feel downcast or abandoned. It's human.

129. Avoid being negative. "An anxious heart weighs a man down, but a kind word cheers him up" (Proverbs 12:25).

130. Understand that there is no "good time" to become chronically ill. Not "while you're young and there is such great research," nor "when you're older and have had a lot of good years anyway."

131. Tell her, "I don't know how you do it all." It's hard work to manage a chronic illness, the paperwork, the side effects, etc., all while feeling miserable and dealing with a declining income.

132. Tell her to feel free to keep a list of things you can help with when you come. Little things like changing a light bulb, hanging a photo, or opening a jar can be impossible for a single person with limited mobility.

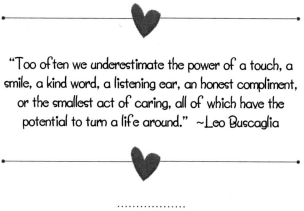

"Too often we underestimate the power of a touch, a smile, a kind word, a listening ear, an honest compliment, or the smallest act of caring, all of which have the potential to turn a life around." ~Leo Buscaglia

133. Give her a special Christmas ornament each year, and write your name and the year on the back.

134. Don't tell her she should avoid medicines that are addictive. Options for pain management are very limited. Let her work out her medical details with a doctor.

135. Ask him to teach your children something: whether it is about a war he fought in, a hobby he enjoys, or how to play checkers. He'll feel like he's participating in life and not just accepting gifts.

136. Try your best to learn to read your friend's body language.

137. When you see him at church, go over and say, "Just seeing you here inspires me. It's hard for me to get here, but when I see you here, I know I can make it through anything."

138. Hire her to do something that you've not been able to accomplish, like putting photos in albums.

139. Bring her a catalog of things she may be interested in, either to order from or just to browse.

Piglet sidled up to Pooh from behind. "Pooh!" he whispered. "Yes, Piglet?" "Nothing," said Piglet, taking Pooh's paw. "I just wanted to be sure of you."
~A. A. Milne

140. Remember not to ask too many questions. Friends don't want to be science projects.

141. Not every piece of correspondence requires a long letter. Include a sticky note with a newspaper clipping, a recipe, an interesting magazine article, or a cartoon; and just write, "Thought you would enjoy this! Thinking of you!"

142. Don't talk with his caregiver as if your friend isn't there.

143. If she likes children bring yours over after they are done with holiday photos to show her the outfits and share a dessert.

144. When you say, "How are you doing?" say it with meaning so he knows that you really do want to know.

145. When she is grieving, bring her a pretty hankie and tell her that it's okay to cry and you thought she should do it in style.

146. Remind her that her heart won't be changed by this illness. "A friend knows the song in my heart and sings it to me when my memory fails." ~Donna Roberts

147. Before holidays, ask her how you can assist. Does she need wrapping paper, supplies for making gifts, boxes? You could take things to the post office and stand in the long lines for her at the same time you send your own packages.

148. Bring her "seasons" inside to experience. Pinecones and nuts, daffodils, or a big snowball for her freezer are all fun.

149. Give her a wind chime for her patio.

150. Teach her how to use a chat room on the Internet or an e-mail group so she can correspond with others who have the same illness and gain supportive friendships.

151. When someone is in the hospital she is often touched only as an "object," not as a person. Ask her, "Can I give you a little hug?"

152. Watch your friend's children so she and her spouse can have a night out.

153. Plant flower bulbs in her yard that will come up in the spring.

154. Books about chronic illness may help you understand a little bit about the life your friend leads, but don't ever use what you've read to prove to her that she is "doing this wrong" or that you are now the expert.

155. If she wants to get or finish an education, encourage her to seek out options. There are many correspondence courses, scholarships, and also disabled student services.

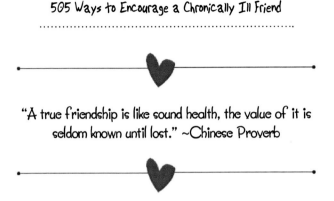

"A true friendship is like sound health, the value of it is seldom known until lost." ~Chinese Proverb

156. Ask, "What could I bring you the next time I come?"

157. Don't share any horror stories: about illness, surgeries, hospitals—nothing.

158. If your pastor's wife has an illness, do not judge your pastor's ministry by her inability to be at every church meeting.

159. Woman to woman, a non-underwire bra can make all the difference when you are bed bound. Try www.wearease.com or www.dreamproductscatalog.com. Dream products also have bra strap adjusters to keep straps up.

160. Help him make calls, and volunteer to sit and be on hold to get insurance questions answered.

161. Don't bring up old grievances.

162. Encourage her to do research on her illness and treatment. Let her know that you believe in her ability to be a great self-advocate.

163. Don't let your fear of not knowing what to say prevent you from keeping in touch.

164. Treat her as though she is still a whole person, despite her limitations.

165. Pray for his medical team.

166. Say, "I've missed seeing you in church. You are such an important part of our fellowship. When you're here I praise God, because I know you are well enough to come. But when you are not here, it prompts me to pray for you."

167. Understand how hard it is to accept help.

168. Don't say, "Oh, you're much too young to have that disease."

169. Offer to clean the shower stall or tub.

Questions to Ask Yourself:
- ⁊ If I felt like I had the flu for months on end, what would cheer me up?
- ⁊ What would my friend say about my presence (or lack of it) in her life?
- ⁊ When is the last time I did something for someone for completely unselfish reasons and not out of obligation?

170. "My command is this: Love each other as I have loved you. Greater love has no one than this, that he lay down his life for his friends" (John 15:12-13).

171. Just accept her, faults and all.

172. Ask, "How is your pain level today?" No one ever asks this and yet his life revolves around it. He'll appreciate your concern!

173. Don't try to figure out God for her. When you don't understand what God is doing in her life, say, "I just don't understand what God is doing in your life. I'm going to continue to pray for your comfort."

174. Avoid sharing about a friend who had the same illness and never missed a day of work.

175. Don't ask him, "Isn't that a woman's disease?"

176. Learn a new craft together. If she has a favorite craft, bring her extra supplies.

177. Never question whether your friend is doing the right thing by trusting "those money-hungry doctors."

178. Pray before you visit, even if it's as you come up the front walkway.

179. If she can't have children, or has decided not to, don't complain about your children or tell her, "You're so lucky to not have to deal with kids."

180. Ask her if she'd like you to help rearrange her furniture for a fresh feeling in her house.

181. Organize a "love shower" and have people send a note/visit/call each day for a month. It's a great way to get one through a difficult time, such as the anniversary of a lost loved one.

182. Give her a box of various greeting cards so she will have some to send to people for last-minute birthdays or events.

183. Bring her the ingredients for a sherbet float and share a summer moment . . . even if it's winter.

184. Buy her a hammer and put a note with it that says, "For picture hanging or other hammer emergencies call (555-your number)."

185. Don't make assumptions. Henry Winkler says, "Assumptions are the termites of relationships."

186. Buy her some new pj's. . . and don't act surprised when she wears them all day.

187. A good attitude doesn't cure an illness, but Proverbs 17:22 says, "A cheerful heart is good medicine." Share your cheerful heart.

188. Bring her some cute refrigerator magnets for photos and cards you will send.

189. Don't assume that just because your ill friend lives with relatives, her basic needs are being taken care of. Often she still fixes her own meals, does laundry, and even goes days without talking with anyone.

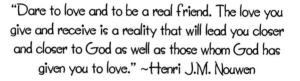

"Dare to love and to be a real friend. The love you give and receive is a reality that will lead you closer and closer to God as well as those whom God has given you to love." ~Henri J.M. Nouwen

190. Don't say, "I'd feel awful too if I was using all of those medications you take!"

191. Be thankful that someone trusts you enough to share his most personal, intimate fears with you.

192. Recognize that there are some very personal factors about living with a chronic illness. When she says, "I need to use the bathroom" don't think that she can just wait.

....

193. Tell her what you've learned from her.

194. "Let your conversation be always full of grace, seasoned with salt, so that you may know how to answer everyone" (Colossians 4:6).

195. Watch for local events that may bring a bit of joy to her life, and rent a wheelchair if necessary. For example, would she love a cat show, a harvest festival, or a local parade? Do something out of the ordinary.

196. Don't just pray for her; pray *with* her.

197. If a massage would feel good (it doesn't always), give her a gift certificate for one.

198. Don't assume that he has plenty of meals delivered and plenty of daily cards. He likely has much less than you believe.

199. Help her with her children's birthday parties— but don't take over; let her make all the decisions.

200. Give her an engraved rock that says something that reminds you of her: courage, cherish, etc.

201. Ask, "What have you had to give up that you really loved?" and then think creatively to see if there is any way you could make some part of that come true.

"We must never minimize the suffering of another. Scripture's mandate to us is, 'Weep with them that weep.'" (Romans 12:15 KJV) ~Billy Graham

202. Don't talk incessantly about your vacation if she is unable to take one.

203. Bring fun decorative lights to hang in her hospital room (but first ask her if it's okay!).

204. Clean the snow off of his walk.

205. Spa jets for a tub can easily make a bathtub into a relaxing "hot tub."

206. If she likes to garden, get her large-handled utensils or a potting table.

207. Allow her to talk about her feelings when she needs to, even if it changes the schedule of the fun that you had planned.

208. Nearly always, a hug is the best response you can give. (Don't squeeze too hard!)

209. Give a gift card to a major variety store for necessities one needs and can't afford.

210. "A friend is one who knows you and loves you just the same." ~Elbert Hubbard

211. Have your spouse take her spouse to play golf or have a guy's day, and keep her company.

212. Say, "I love day-old microwaved coffee" and make huge delicious slurping noises.

213. Buy her a colorful flag for her patio.

214. Don't say, "God must be withholding your healing for a reason."

215. Remember, it takes so little effort and time out of your life to change someone else's life.

216. Don't say, "Well, at least you aren't bedridden!"

217. Ask her, "What motivates you to keep going when you are feeling down?" She's a great source of encouragement when you need a pick-me-up.

218. Bring a journal for her hospital room and have visitors leave notes of encouragement to her in it. It helps to have everyone answer a question such as, "One of my favorite memories of our time together is . . ." and "If I had my wish, when you are out of this hospital we would . . ."

219. Look for her hidden talents and encourage her to pursue them.

220. He knows you can't fix the illness and he doesn't even want you to try. It's okay.

221. Bring her a miniature Christmas tree during the holidays.

222. Remember John 9:3: " 'Neither this man nor his parents sinned,' said Jesus, 'but this happened so that the work of God might be displayed in his life.' "

223. Validate his worth by allowing him to do what he can do for himself.

224. Ask her what toy she loved as a child or what she never got and always wanted. For a special gift, see if you can find it on an online auction.

225. Ask friends if they would like to donate toward a weekend away for your friend with her spouse. Those with chronic illness rarely have extra funds to take even a short vacation.

226. Remember her birthday and don't make fun of her age. With chronic illness, one is happy to still be around, and one already feels much older than one's age.

227. Perk up her patio with flowers and furniture.

"Remember that everyone you meet is afraid of something, loves something, and has lost something."
~H. Jackson Brown Jr.

228. Bring over a special home-baked dessert if you know she is having company.

229. Recognize that gifts of food aren't really about the food—they are about nourishing one's soul and feeding love.

230. If she is stuck in bed, make it comfortable. Bring extra pillows, a heating pad, a writing tray, or a water carafe.

231. Hold yourself together. Don't become so upset over his illness that he has to take care of you.

232. Ask her, "Would you like me to find out what some of the local support services are for someone with your illness?"

233. Give her a devotional book for someone with a chronic illness. See www.comfortzonebooks.com.

234. Help her hook up her sprinkler system on a timer so she doesn't have to manually water.

235. Encourage her to get second opinions on her health just to be safe.

236. Acknowledge every success she has—no matter how small.

237. Don't abandon a friendship just because there are awkward moments as you are both adjusting to the illness. They will pass and you'll be able to even laugh about them later.

238. If she's lonely, encourage her to sponsor a child from another country. A great option is www.worldvision.org. Offer to split the cost.

239. If she has to go to the hospital, volunteer to be the center of the phone tree on her progress, or if you're web savvy, ask her if you can set up a web site for people to check in with her.

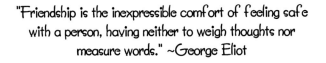

"Friendship is the inexpressible comfort of feeling safe with a person, having neither to weigh thoughts nor measure words." ~George Eliot

240. Don't offer pity. Don't say, "Oh, poor baby."

241. Arrange a monthly housekeeping service.

....

242. If you drop by unannounced, feel her out to see if she needs you to stay or to leave. If there is any doubt say, "I've only got a few minutes, but I'd love for us to make time together soon. When would work for you?"

243. Offer to read to her.

244. Have reasonable expectations. You may feel like you are giving more than you are receiving sometimes. "Blessed is he who is kind to the needy" (Proverbs 14:21).

245. Help her organize her closets, especially for new seasons when she may need help getting things down from a shelf or out from under a bed.

246. Don't say, "You shouldn't be doing _____." She's made her choice for a specific reason. (Many homeschooling mothers who are ill get weary of this comment.)

247. Ask him, "If you could choose the headline for tomorrow's paper, what would it be?"

248. Linen spray makes a fun gift to perk up the sheets.

249. Don't relentlessly complain about your job if she's not able to work.

250. "Trust in the Lord with all your heart and lean not on your own understanding" (Proverbs 3:5,6).

251. For a special gift, ask friends to write on an index card something your friend has done that has encouraged them: an encouraging word or Scripture, a cartoon, or anything; and then bind them in an album.

252. If he has vision problems, order some good books and magazines in large print.

253. Invite her to dinner at your house and let her know you are blessed with her presence. (Don't expect a return invitation.)

254. Resist the temptation to say, "If you just had more faith . . . or prayed harder . . ."

255. If you are short on time, just pray together as you're driving to the doctor's appointment.

256. If she cannot afford it, give her Internet service so she can connect with other people online.

257. A charm bracelet makes a fun gift. You can add charms to celebrate events in her life that symbolize hope, survival, joy. and celebrations.

258. Make her a quilt and tell her you prayed for her while you stitched.

259. Take her to the ballet. Emphasize, "I really want you to be able to enjoy it, so let's leave whenever you start to get physically uncomfortable. We don't have to stay for all of it if you feel it's too much."

Reflect on this statement:
"The first question that the priest and the Levite asked was: 'If I stop to help this man, what will happen to me?' But. . . the good Samaritan reversed the question: 'If I do not stop to help this man, what will happen to him?' " ~Martin Luther King Jr.

260. If you buy her a magazine subscription, make a note to yourself to renew it the next year. She may not be able to afford to but will be too embarrassed to ask.

261. Remember friendship isn't made up of one big thing you do, but a hundred little things.

262. Introduce her to some good fiction novels.

263. Give her fun pens and pencils.

264. Go eat lunch at a restaurant overlooking a serene golf course. It's a peaceful way to spend an afternoon.

265. Ask, "How can I support you best?"

266. Recognize that she may be wrapped up in her own life right now, but she will never forget the love you've shown her, and she'll be there when you need her.

267. Make sure she has a cell phone that works, even if she uses it only for emergencies.

268. Remind her how much she has taught you about life!

269. Bring one of your pets to visit. Be sure to leave it in the car and ask first if she would like to come out or if you can bring it in. A cuddle with a furry friend can do wonders.

270. Never assume that her illness is caused by a lack of faith. It takes a great deal of faith to live in so much pain and still trust God each morning.

271. Don't interrupt. "He who answers before listening—that is his folly and his shame" (Proverbs 18:13).

272. Say, "I think you are coping amazingly well given all the circumstances. I hope you'll be there to encourage me someday when I'm falling apart. I really admire you."

273. Send her a valentine.

274. Feeling grumpy yourself? Some advice by an unknown author is "Never miss an opportunity to make others happy, even if you have to leave them alone in order to do it."

275. Tell her when you will be out of town or not able to be reached, especially if you are her emergency contact.

276. Remember, your time is *always* more important to her than any amount of money you will spend.

277. "Therefore encourage one another and build each other up, just as in fact you are doing" (1 Thessalonians 5:11).

278. Participate in an illness "walk."

279. Volunteer to watch her children a couple of times each month so she can go get lab work done, MRIs—whatever she needs to do, and have a few minutes of time to herself.

280. Recognize that what she could do yesterday may not be possible today. Don't question that. Every day is different.

281. She needs someone to just share things to make them "real." Miles Franklin says, "Someone to tell it to is one of the fundamental needs of human beings."

282. Bring note cards and stamps. She may want to encourage someone else or write thank-you notes to those who have helped her.

283. If she tries to make you feel guilty by sarcastically saying, "Sorry to be such a burden," simply say, "I'm so sorry you feel that way. You aren't a burden, and I'm failing if I'm making you feel that way. How can I change?"

284. Never ask, "How much weight have you gained since your prognosis?"

285. If her relationship with the Lord is questionable at the time, don't lecture her, but be there with unconditional love. "A despairing man should have the devotion of his friends, even though he forsakes the fear of the Almighty" (Job 6:14).

286. Never say, "Gee, it must be nice to just stay home and take a nap!"

287. Keep in mind that one's physical health can directly impact her mental health. Give her some space to grieve and understand her new identity as someone with physical limitations.

288. If you can't accommodate her joyfully, don't help at all. Being helped out by someone grudgingly is deeply painful.

289. Do a crossword puzzle together.

290. Remember, the illness may actually be God's will for his life. Don't wait for him to be healed in order to "start his life."

"The best kind of friend is the one you could sit on a porch with, never saying a word, and walk away feeling like that was the best conversation you've had."
~Author Unknown

---

291. Don't say, "If you'd just get some exercise you'd probably feel a lot better" or "Aren't there any exercises that will help with your pain?"

292. Don't distance yourself out of guilt or embarrassment over a comment or situation. Just apologize and move on.

293. Though it may be true, don't live this way: "It's so much easier to pray for a bore than to go and see him." C. S. Lewis, *Into The Wardrobe*

....

294. Help her start a collection of things she likes if she doesn't yet have one.

295. Show her how to order groceries online and have them delivered to her house.

296. Bring her videos of events that she cannot attend, like a Women of Faith conference. Ask if you can stay and watch a bit with her to share the experience.

297. Pray that her children will understand God's love for them and their ill parent.

298. Ask him what makes him feel cared for and then remember his answer.

299. Give her a special bookmark.

300. "This is what the Lord says: 'Stand at the crossroads and look; ask for the ancient paths, ask where the good way is, and walk in it, and you will find rest for your souls' " (Jeremiah 6:16a).

301. Offer to write letters for her. Handwriting can be difficult.

302. Don't come and visit for hours. It's hard for people to ask you to leave.

303. If you haven't been in contact for some time, it's never too late. Send a card that says, "I'm so, so sorry I haven't been there for you, but I have been thinking of you and praying for you. I'd love to see you." Then follow up with a call in a couple of days.

304. Clip cartoons that will make her smile.

305. Ask her, "I know when I invite you to go somewhere there will be a lot of times you'll have to pass. But I enjoy your company and hope someday you'll say yes. So is it okay if I keep asking?"

306. Don't worry . . . you won't catch it.

307. Ask her where she has always wanted to go for vacation and then do your best to bring it to her. Call the visitor's bureau or library and get videos, brochures, and books. Bring them over to her house with an authentic meal from the place and watch the videos.

308. Give her a cute night-light and write in a card, "You light up my life!"

Help with a happy heart. "The King will reply, 'I tell you the truth, whatever you did for one of the least of these brothers of mine, you did for me.' . . . He will reply, 'I tell you the truth, whatever you did not do for one of the least of these, you did not do it for me.' "
(Matthew 25:40, 45)

309. Have your child pick out an item that will make her smile. For example, Veggie Tales videos of "Silly Songs" leave adults roaring with laughter.

310. Don't say, "What did you do so wrong to suffer like this?" (Yes, people ask this.)

311. Ask her if she'd like you to pick up her children for Sunday school when she can't go.

....

312. Discover her dietary restrictions and then bring her a treat she can eat.

313. Realize that the person who lives with chronic illness and pain probably needs you much more than the one going through a short-lived crisis. Many people are probably ministering to the one in the much-publicized crisis.

314. Give her a break. "The essence of true friendship is to make allowance for another's little lapses." ~David Storey

315. Try to understand that just returning a phone call may seem overwhelming to her. Don't judge her actions based on past habits.

316. When you leave ask, "Do you have mail I could drop off for you?"

317. Allow God to work in his life without making your friend feel that God is judging him.

318. There is not a quick fix for the illness, so avoid getting too excited about vinegar remedies, green tea, or bee stings, etc.

319. Bring her something that will make her laugh, a silly gift that is out of character for both of you.

320. Remember you could be in her shoes at any moment. "The difference between a helping hand and an outstretched palm is a twist of the wrist." ~Laurence Leamer, *King of the Night*

321. Learn how to spell and pronounce the name of your friend's illness. It's courteous.

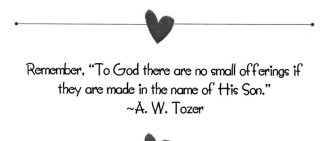

Remember, "To God there are no small offerings if they are made in the name of His Son."
~A. W. Tozer

322. Send notes consistently. The "not forgetting her" is what *really* matters.

323. Give him a pedicure—yes, men need pedicures too!

324. Use Scripture only to comfort him. Don't use it to prove your point or convince him of a decision he should make.

325. When you are together assume you will take the elevator, and don't complain about how far it is out of your way.

326. "Here is a test to find whether your mission on earth is finished: If you're alive, it isn't."
~ Richard Bach

327. Take photos of a special event and laminate a collage of them for a place mat for casual meals.

328. Recognize that going on financial disability assistance is an emotional process. She may grieve that she "qualifies."

329. Ask her to pray for you and your concerns. It's not all about her (really . . . it's not), and she'll be glad to. She doesn't want to be sheltered from what's going on in your life.

330. If you start your sentence by saying, "I probably shouldn't say this . . ." then don't!

331. Know her preferences. If she doesn't like teddy bears, don't buy her a teddy bear, no matter how cute he is.

332. Bring her a bed tray with a cloth napkin, a flower, and a note.

333. Select things you can do for her and make up little coupons. It's much easier for a friend to express her needs without feeling guilty this way.

334. Remember, it's sometimes those who annoy us the most that God is calling us to minister to. "Kindness is in our power, even when fondness is not. ~Samuel Johnson

335. Help her clean out dresser drawers and line them with scented paper.

336. Watch her favorite home movies with her and let her tell you who everyone is and her favorite memories.

337. If you are involved in church ministry, ask her "What do you think God is calling you to do as part of our congregation, and what can we do to help you accomplish that?"

338. Arrange to have a panel of people who live with illness at your church get together and encourage her to participate to share her expertise at coping with difficulties. Say, "I know others would be inspired by you and your attitude."

339. Don't pretend the illness doesn't exist and don't act like that's all she is about now. Tell her if you feel awkward about how to address it.

340. Accept her for who she is and just spend time with her. You don't always have to do something to show you care.

341. Christmas carol at her house.

342. "Be joyful in hope, patient in affliction, faithful in prayer" (Romans 12:12).

343. Give her a copy of this book and tell her to check off anything that would be meaningful for her.

344. Recognize that being a friend to a chronically ill person can be wearying, but you'll end up richly rewarded in ways you never imagined.

345. Allow her the occasional pity party on your shoulder without your advice or perky attitude.

346. Be on time when you make a commitment to her, and don't be upset with her if she is late.

Before speaking, ask yourself:
T—Is it true?
H—Is it helpful?
I—Is it inspiring?
N—Is it necessary?
K—Is it kind?

347. If she can no longer make her famous "dish" for family gatherings, volunteer to come over and make it at her house while she gives you instructions.

348. Help her color or highlight her hair.

349. Ask, "How can I pray for you this week?"

350. Buy her a towel warmer and fluffy new towels.

351. "Two are better than one, because they have a good return for their work: if one falls down, his friend can help him up. But pity the man who falls and has no one to help him up!" (Ecclesiastes 4:9-10).

352. Take her needs seriously. If she can't have sugar, don't just "slip a little in." It could have dire consequences.

353. Consider yourself a friend for the journey—not a physician nor a savoir.

354. Don't act better than her just because you can see her dust balls and dirty walls.

355. Leave a May Day basket on her doorstep.

356. Give her a jar of encouragement. Fill a jar with slips of paper each bearing encouragement, such as verses from the Bible or positive sayings. Tell her whenever she is feeling down to pull out a word of encouragement.

357. Ask, "What Scriptures are getting you through this time?"

358. Find out what games she likes to play. If visitors arrive and there is an uncomfortable silence, a game of backgammon may help lighten the atmosphere.

359. Don't use your prayer time with her as a chance to preach a sermon "to God" for her benefit.

360. When she does something for you, like making dinner or a craft project say, "I know how much trouble you went to for me, because you did this despite the pain you are in. I want you to know how much I appreciate it."

361. When she feels guilty for canceling plans on you say, "I understand that your illness is very unpredictable. We'll miss you!"

362. When he makes corny jokes about his hair falling out from drugs or getting injections of medication, don't gasp in surprise; just laugh along.

363. Remember that weather can dramatically alter how one feels physically. A bit of rain could make him bed bound for a few days.

364. "If one of you says to him, 'Go, I wish you well; keep warm and well fed,' but does nothing about his physical needs, what good is it?" (James 2:16).

365. When she says, "I need to get something to eat," accommodate her as quickly as possible. Blood sugar can drop quickly and have serious consequences.

Don't feel like you need to do something extravagant. "He who waits to do a great deal of good at once will never do anything." ~Samuel Johnson

366. Understand the difference between empathy and sympathy.

367. Remember, "Advice is like snow; the softer it falls, the deeper it goes. The longer it dwells upon, and sinks into the mind." ~Samuel Taylor Coleridge

368. Maintain eye contact when she's talking. Don't be thinking about what advice you're going to give as soon as she pauses.

369. Bring something simple but symbolic when you visit.

370. Ralph Waldo Emerson says, "The only gift is a portion of thyself."

371. If mail is stacking up and it's obvious no one is able to help, offer to go through it for her and separate the trash from what can go into folders. Some people get depressed and overwhelmed by it all and just need a fresh "system."

372. When you pray for him, remember to pray for his family (children and spouse as well as parents and siblings). It will bring him comfort because he's worried about how his illness is impacting their lives.

373. Don't make him prove that his illness is legitimate.

374. "Do everything without complaining or arguing" (Philippians 2:14).

375. If her spouse is not a Christian or isn't support6ive, pray for and with her about it. Tell her she can call you whenever she needs spiritual fellowship—living in a marriage without spiritual harmony can be very lonely.

376. Encourage him to write a book. Even a few copies of a memoir can easily be printed and shared with family members. For example, www.instantpublisher.com is a great printer with reasonable prices.

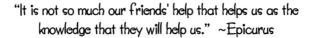

"It is not so much our friends' help that helps us as the knowledge that they will help us." ~Epicurus

377. Books on tape make great gifts.

378. Bring something silly to the hospital that she can use to break the ice with other visitors. Ideas: cartoon bandages for her IVs, silly slippers, a sign for the door, flamingo lights.

....

379. Consider this: When you say, "I know God will heal you; you're such a good person," what kind of person will she feel like if God doesn't heal her?

380. Suffering is humbling. Recognize he may be embarrassed to accept your help. Don't make a big deal out of it.

381. Recognize that each chronically ill person has different needs. One kind of encouragement doesn't work for everyone.

382. If you are musical bring her a gift of your music. Play the guitar, piano, or just sing a song.

383. Time doesn't always heal all wounds. Don't tell her in time she will "get over it."

384. Do what you do out of love, not to feel good about yourself.

385. Get her a comfortable, padded rocking chair for her patio.

386. Ask, "How are your family members handling your illness? How can I pray for them?"

....

387. Recognize that you aren't necessarily supposed to "cheer someone up." Your presence should be about offering comfort, validating one's feelings, and giving unconditional love.

388. Give gift certificates to the local fast-food restaurants for a quick meal.

389. Help her put together a collage of photos of family and friends, ticket stubs, and other sentimental items in a scrapbook. It will be something to gaze at when she is feeling down.

390. Clean out her refrigerator and swear that yours has looked much worse.

391. Offer to help install assistive devices like handrails.

392. Paint her toenails and add decals for fun.

393. Give her rubber stamps and ink. They are fun to use on cards.

394. Never flirt with the person's spouse, even if you are all good friends and it's harmless.

395. Never—*ever*—tell her it's all in her head.

....

396. Validate her feelings by saying, "That would scare me too," not "You shouldn't be afraid."

397. Ask how you should pray. Don't assume that you know in what way your friend desires prayer.

398. We all stick our feet in our mouth. When it happens, acknowledge it, apologize immediately, and say, "I just wasn't thinking."

399. "They set out from their homes and met together by agreement to go and sympathize with him and comfort him. When they saw him from a distance, they could hardly recognize him. . . . Then they sat on the ground with him for seven days and seven nights. No one said a word to him, because they saw how great was his suffering" (Job 2:11-13).

400. Stick around for the long haul. Few friends don't make the effort.

401. If she starts using an assistive device, like a cane, don't make a big deal out of it.

402. Few people qualify for financial disability assistance upon application. Don't act shocked if she gets an attorney to help with her case.

403. Before she checks out of the hospital offer to bring home her flowers and plants. Take them to her house and place them in different rooms.

404. Give her a biography of how someone overcame a challenge, like *Joni.*

405. Remember, you may be the only "Jesus" she sees visibly acting in her life right now.

406. Talk about normal everyday things, not just the illness.

407. Encourage her to follow new dreams. Does she like writing? Photography? Help her discover her passions.

408. If you plan to go somewhere, don't try to outdo her in your outfit. She may be grieving the loss of her previous appearance and what she was able to wear (like normal shoes).

409. Just show up! Phone calls are nice but visiting in person is so much more intimate.

"A real friend is one who walks in when the rest of the world walks out. Friendship is one mind in two bodies."
~Mencius

410. Romans 12:15 says, "Rejoice with those who rejoice; mourn with those who mourn." Don't forget to have rejoicing be part of your friendship.

411. Don't act shocked that your friend may be on at least fifteen drugs. It takes a lot of medication to manage a chronic illness and its side effects.

412. You don't have to have money to encourage someone. It's about your presence, not your presents.

413. Being housebound can feel depressing. Bring her seasonal items so she has new surroundings. For example, a new tablecloth or place mats, a candle or room fragrance, a beverage mix and mug, lotions, and in-season fruit.

414. Don't talk about the seriousness of her illness in front of her children.

415. Recognize that if this is a new relationship you'll likely feel awkward in her presence at first. It will get easier.

416. Help clean her house before out-of-town guests arrive.

417. When he cries, just sit with him. You don't need to do anything. Don't tell him, "Don't cry" or "This isn't worth crying about."

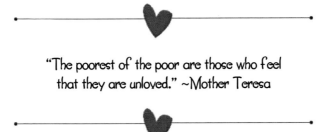

"The poorest of the poor are those who feel that they are unloved." ~Mother Teresa

418. Say, "This all frightens me too, but we'll get through it together. I'm not going anywhere!"

419. Don't finish her sentences.

420. Host a party for one of her friends. Let her do the planning of theme, decorations, menu, etc. and then help her make it happen.

421. Don't ever smoke in her presence.

422. Offer to change her sheets. This is an impossible task for many people with chronic illness but an awkward task to ask for help with.

423. When you see a commercial for a drug she is on, remember that life is not always like the commercials. The people in the commercials are actors pretending to be in pain.

424. Help her children pick out gifts for her on special occasions like Mother's Day.

425. Tell him you will pray for him at a specific time that is important to him, such as during a medical exam or while he's waiting for test results.

426. Don't say, "Sometimes I don't feel like getting up in the morning and going to church after the week I've had, but I do it anyway. So why don't you just pull yourself together and set your alarm and come?"

427. If you believe he would be a great mentor, tell him!

428. "Go the extra mile. It's never crowded."
~Author Unknown

429. If you say, "Call me anytime you need something," do your best to follow through when she calls. Don't act like her request is inconvenient. You'll never know how hard it was for her to pick up the phone.

"Make it a rule, and pray to God to help you to keep it, never, if possible, to lie down at night without being able to say: 'I have made one human being at least a little wiser, or a little happier, or at least a little better this day.' " ~Charles Kingsley

430. If she wants a walking buddy, be one!

431. Blankets are always cozy gifts.

432. Include a single friend in your family gatherings, even if he comes for only an hour.

433. Say, "I wish I knew what to say, but I don't. I'm here for you, though."

434. Understand that your friend is constantly forced to choose the amount of things she can do in one day, against the amount of pain she will suffer the next few days. Some days plans with you will "win"—some days not. It's not personal.

435. Sometimes a neighbor can be more help than a sibling. Proverbs 27:10 says, "Do not go to your brother's house when disaster strikes you— better a neighbor nearby than a brother far away."

436. Remember that you are a guest in her home. If you bring something for dinner ask her, "May I put this in your fridge?" Don't just run to the refrigerator.

437. Don't tell her most illnesses are caused by stress, even if you read that in a reliable publication.

....

438. Never assume someone who parks in a disabled parking place is "faking" just because you don't see any assistive devices.

439. Pray a specific Scripture for your friend and then write her a note with that Scripture and let her know you are praying for her.

440. Avoid giving "God balm." If you say, "God will heal you" or "All things work together . . ." she will believe you don't really understand and will avoid sharing her feelings with you in the future.

441. If you invite her to an event ask her, "Is there someone you would like to invite? I'd be happy to pick her up too."

"A friend accepts us as we are yet helps us to be what we should." ~Author Unknown

442. Don't say, "Are you sure you can't find *some* work to do?"

....

443. Remind her that God has great plans for her life, even if they seem invisible right now. Tell her she's still living in God's Plan A; the illness didn't come as a surprise to Him, so He's not trying to figure out what to do with her life.

444. Plant a tree in her yard (with her permission) to celebrate something, like a year of being cancer-free.

445. Don't make him feel guilty for being ill. Many people believe if a friend isn't willing to try every "cure" under the sun he must actually "want" to be ill. That's crazy talk!

446. When you visit, leave behind a little gift or a note for her to find later.

447. Help make sure her home is secure so she feels safe. Install locks, alarms, and check smoke alarms batteries.

448. "Accept one another, then, just as Christ accepted you, in order to bring praise to God" (Roman 5:7).

449. Give her a copy of your favorite worship CD.

450. Have someone paint a mural of her favorite scenery on her bedroom wall.

451. Give her the most comfortable seat in the car. Don't make her climb over your kids' toys and car seat and squeeze in the back.

452. Understand that alternative medicines carry great risks too. People with chronic illness frequently weigh the benefits with the consequences when making decisions.

453. Try to see the world through her eyes. How would you feel if tomorrow you suddenly couldn't stand, if you forgot your children's names, or had to quit your job?

454. Ask if he would want Communion brought to him while at home or in the hospital, and then arrange this with his church.

455. Give her a little basket of bath goodies, such as soaps, shower gels, and lotions.

456. Bring cookies, but say that it's because your family doesn't enjoy this kind.

457. Don't ask, "How long have you got left to live?"

"The friend who holds your hand and says the wrong thing is made of dearer stuff than the one who stays away." ~Barbara Kingsolver

458. When she says, "My garden is overflowing with weeds . . ." she's trying to figure out a way to ask if you or someone you know could help with this task.

459. Never say, "You need to get over this and move on." Just be her friend. Everyone grieves differently.

460. If you send her e-mails, don't just forward all your "junk mail" because you think she would enjoy it. Take the time to make it a personal note. Also, don't forward e-mails written by her to others without her permission.

461. Pretend her messy house doesn't bother you.

462. Go with her to the doctor and then go get coffee or lunch afterward. Medical visits get lonely and depressing.

463. Encourage her to barter her services for help in other areas. Is she a great cook, an accountant, a graphic designer, an editor? Maybe she could trade for housekeeping or gardening.

464. Make a soup basket with mugs, bowls, soups, crackers, and a note that says, "Your strength just bowls me over!"

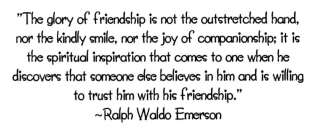

"The glory of friendship is not the outstretched hand, nor the kindly smile, nor the joy of companionship; it is the spiritual inspiration that comes to one when he discovers that someone else believes in him and is willing to trust him with his friendship."
~Ralph Waldo Emerson

465. Make her a CD of inspirational music that has gotten you through tough times.

466. Understand the signs of depression, and tell him it's a normal reaction to the circumstances. Encourage him to talk to his doctor or pastor about his feelings.

467. Bring him a sports-bloopers video.

468. Teach her how to use the Internet so she can learn more about her illness from medical web sites.

469. Be reliable. Don't cancel because "something better" came up.

470. Bring her a silly toy just for fun. A Magnadoodle or a Mr. Potato Head may be good for a laugh.

471. Take her to the cosmetics counter of a retail store. Oftentimes they offer free hand massages, facials, or beauty tips.

472. Stand up for her when others make ignorant remarks about her illness in your presence.

473. Remember to always have a no-alcoholic beverage available for her.

474. Make sure she can vote. Drive her to the polls or let her know how to get a ballot by mail.

475. Ask "How can I help you make her home feel more like a retreat? What would you change if you could?" and then help her make it possible.

476. Buy her a CD player for her shower and some worship music to start the day off uplifted.

477. Ask her if she (and her family) would like to go to the fair with your family, even if they meet you for only a couple of hours.

478. Give her a journal and write something encouraging on the first page.

479. Bring her a living Easter basket from a florist.

480. Remember, you don't have to be a perfect friend. You don't need to do everything in this book, just a few things consistently.

481. Don't get angry or huffy when she doesn't take your good advice.

482. Ask, "How far can you walk comfortably?" Don't take any amount for granted.

483. Have your children make an encouragement card for the entire family and leave it on their doorstep with dinner and include a special treat just for the kids.

"Never let a problem to be solved become more important than a person to be loved."
~Barbara Johnson

484. Recognize how deeply lonely illness can be. "A poor man's friend deserts him" (Proverbs 19:4).

485. Understand that being chronically ill and being sick are two different things. When your friend is both sick *and* ill she desperately needs you.

486. Leave an encouraging message on her answering machine when you know she will be

....

gone so that she comes home to a message of warmth.

487. Give her a ride to the airport when needed. When you pick her up, have a snack and a pillow for the car ride home.

488. Ask for her help on a project.

489. Seek refreshment! Proverbs 11:25 says, "He who refreshes others will himself be refreshed."

490. Take her for a ride in the country or to see the sunset at the beach. A simple outing is a wonderful afternoon away from the house.

491. Have a "un-birthday party"—just to celebrate her.

492. Cry with her.

493. Sing praises with her over good news.

494. Understand that she may have to be very limited to sun exposure, if any. Ask her if she has concerns.

495. Bring a big basket with a bow to her hospital room to keep all the gifts in that other people are bringing her, some stamped note cards, and a notebook for people to write messages in if she's sleeping during their visits.

THINGS TO WRITE IN CARDS:

496. I know it must seem like God is distant right now, but maybe He is just working undercover in your life. He says, "Never will I leave you; never will I forsake you" (Hebrews 13:5), and I believe this to be true. I pray you will feel His presence.

497. "Do not be discouraged for the Lord your God will be with you wherever you go" (Joshua 1:9b). I know it feels lonely, but God is near and so am I. I will call you tomorrow to see how you are doing.

498. I pray for you each day while I _____. I wanted you to know that this week I have been praying that _____.

....

499. Psalm 34:18: "The Lord is close to the brokenhearted and saves those who are crushed in spirit." I know it may seem dark right now, but I believe God is running toward you to hold you in His arms through this. And my arms are available anytime to give you a big hug!

500. Job was one of God's greatest servants, and even he said, "What strength do I have, that I should still hope? What prospects, that I should be patient?" (Job 6:11). Don't be too hard on yourself during this time of transition. I love you know matter what.

501. I'm so sorry to hear you haven't been sleeping well. I've heard the saying, "Take your problems to the Lord. He's up all night anyway." Know that you are in my prayers. Psalm 4:8 says, "I will like down and sleep in peace, for you alone, O Lord, make me dwell in safety." I pray that God will bring you this peaceful sleep soon.

502. I know it is a lonely time right now. I am here to help however I can, even if you just want someone to hang out with you. Would you enjoy dinner at our home Saturday evening for a couple of hours? We'd be glad to pick you up. We want to hear how you are feeling, any frustrations you may have, or even what God may be teaching you through this experience.

503. "A cheerful heart is good medicine!" (Proverbs 17:22a). I saw this _____ and thought it would bring some cheer to your day!

504. I just wanted you to know I am thinking of you. Second Corinthians 4:16 says, "Therefore we do not lose heart. Though outwardly we are wasting away, yet inwardly we are being renewed day by day." Don't lose heart! I know God has some purpose in all of this, and I pray that you will feel His promised renewal soon.

505. It must seem confusing right now not being able to go to work every day, but I know you have amazing talents that God is not going to waste. First Corinthians 12:6 says, "There are different kinds of working, but the same God works all of them in all men." Hang in there! I pray God will reveal the work He has planned for you soon!

SPECIAL THANKS

Thank you to the following who shared their ideas: Jeanne Campbell - Mary Lou Cornish - Roxanne Creath - Renee Dahlen - Carol Dildine – Joy Easton - Cheryl Edmiston - Anastasia Edwards - Candy Feathers - Lucille Gay - Kathy Guzzo - Dee Harvey - Heidi Henkelman - Lee Herring - Ramona Justice - Mary Jo Lamberts -Ada Mahle - Julie Munroe - Tricia Patterson -  Carole Prior - Glenda Rains - Susan Sumrall - Ginamarie Trombetta - Wendy Thorenz - Holly Timpson - Linda Tinder - Joan Vendlinger - Judy Wainscott

ADDITIONAL COPIES

This is a great book to share with others and we encourage you pass them around to friends, pastors, doctors, and more. We've priced them at a discount for multiple copies: Order online at www.comfortzonebooks.com or call 888-751-7378. You may also send your check, money order or Visa/MC to: REST MINISTRIES, PO Box 502928, San Diego, CA 92150. All proceeds benefit the programs of Rest Ministries, Inc. and National Invisible Chronic Illness Awareness Week

WOULD YOUR ORGANIZATION LIKE PERSONALIZED COPIES?

This book is available as a premium items for your organization or company. Contact us for pricing of bulk copies that can be personalized with a foreword by your president, your logo, contact information, etc.

This book makes a great volunteer gift, a bonus gift with membership dues, a training manual or a conference gift bag insert.
Contact us for information:

Lisa Copen, Rest Ministries Publishers
888-751-7378

NATIONAL INVISIBLE CHRONIC ILLNESS AWARENESS WEEK

National Invisible Chronic Illness Awareness Week, held annually in September, is a designated time worldwide in which people who live with chronic illness, those who love them, and organizations are encouraged to educate the general public, churches, health care professionals, and government officials about the effects of living with a disease that is not visually apparent. For more information visit www.invisibleillness.com or contact Rest Ministries, the sponsor of this week at 888-751-7378.

ABOUT REST MINISTRIES

Rest Ministries, Inc. is a non-profit Christian organization that exists to serve people who live with chronic illness or pain, and their families, by providing spiritual, emotional, relational, and practical support through a variety of resources, including *HopeKeepers® Magazine*, Bible studies, and small group materials.

We also seek to bring an awareness and a change in action throughout churches in the U.S., in regard to how people who live with chronic illness or pain are served, and teach churches effective ministry tools in ministering to this population.

HOPEKEEPERS® MAGAZINE

Designed with your specific needs in mind, *HopeKeepers* will encourage you on your Christian walk while you live with chronic illness and pain. Practical tools and inspiration make this a can't- miss magazine!

- Articles about the things that matter to you: faith, feelings, friends, family, and finances
- Devotionals
- Alternative medicine—biblical perspectives of when it helps and when it hurts
- Peer advice about living with chronic illness and growing in your faith
- Book excerpts and reviews
- Interviews with celebrities and hidden heroes.
- Updates on HopeKeepers groups and how to start a HopeKeepers ministry
- Q/A with a Christian doctor/caregivers column
- Tools to help you become a strong advocate for quality health care
- Published quarterly, approximately 64 pages; $17.97/4 issues; To order by credit card call 888-751-7378 or visit www.restministries.org; or send check, money order or Visa/MC to: REST MINISTRIES, PO Box 502928, San Diego, CA 92150

MORE BOOKS FROM REST MINISTRIES

Order at www.comfortzonebooks.com or 888-751-7378. Web site has complete descriptions and possible discounts on books.

Mosaic Moments: Devotionals for the Chronically Ill, 212 pages, $15

Why Can't I Make People Understand? Discovering the validation those with chronic illness seek and why, 138 pages, $14

Bible Studies:
(1) When Chronic Illness Enters Your Life (2) Learning to Live with Chronic Illness, $6.50 each, 5 lessons each for individuals or groups

So You Want to Start a Chronic Illness/Pain Ministry: 10 Essentials to Make it Work, 80 pages, $15.00

NOTES

JOY COUPON *

Just Offering You....